Richie Was Rich in Blessings

Trilogy Christian Publishers
A Wholly Owned Subsidary of Trinity Broadcasting Network
2442 Michelle Drive
Tustin, CA 92780

For information, address Trilogy Christian Publishing
Rights Department, 2442 Michelle Drive, Tustin, Ca 92780.
Trilogy Christian Publishing/ TBN and colophon are trademarks of Trinity Broadcasting Network.

For information about special discounts for bulk purchases, please contact Trilogy Christian Publishing.

Manufactured in the United States of America

10 9 8 7 6 5 4 3 2 1

Library of Congress Cataloging-in-Publication Data is available.

ISBN 978-1-64773-255-4 (Print Book)
ISBN 978-1-64773-256-1 (ebook)

Richie Was Rich in Blessings

Lisa Collier

1

Richie was a young boy who wanted to do everything by himself.

He would dress himself, but his shirt would be on backwards.

His pants would be inside out.

Sometimes his shoes would be on the wrong feet, and sometimes he would even be missing his socks.

As he would walk down the street, everyone would be nice to Richie, but they would wonder, *Why is his shirt on backwards? Why are his pants on inside out? Why are his shoes on the wrong feet? Can't he feel how uncomfortable that is?* Richie couldn't see or feel how wrong things were.

As time went on, Richie could feel that his shirt was starting to pull on his neck. He felt that it was choking him. *Was something wrong?*

Then his pants were pulling in the wrong direction. *Was something wrong?*

Richie started to get blisters on his feet. *Was something wrong?*

Richie's mom said, "Richie, I know you like to do things on your own, but it's best to have help. You should pray to God to help you in your morning prayers."

Richie began his day in prayer asking for guidance and direction in all things, even down to the smallest of things.

Richie now wears his shirt and pants right side out, and he wears his shoes on the correct feet. "Wow," Richie said, "I feel so much better!"

As he passed everyone on the street, they noticed that Richie looked so much better!

Richie Was Rich in Blessings!